The Grimoire of Forgotten Fairytales

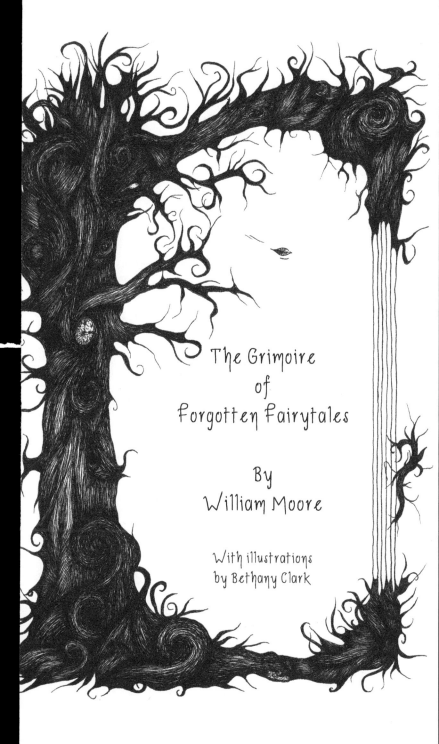

The Grimoire
of
Forgotten Fairytales

By

William Moore

With illustrations
by Bethany Clark

www.williammooremusic.com

Cover and Illustrations by Bethany Clark

First edition

Published by Precipice

Hardback ISBN: 978-1-7395164-0-6

For each and every one of you Who sacrificed your
soul to bring this project to life.

Gathered in the Grimoire, tales that twist and twine,
Lurking in the shadows, where no light dares to shine.
Beneath the gilded pages, forgotten lore abounds,
Its power quietly creeping, as the heart profoundly pounds.

Reached a sacred milestone, the target we've struck true,
Ten thousand souls now tethered, to the ancient and the new.
But tread lightly, dear friend, for the Grimoire's might unfurls,
In the echoes of our victory, as the abyss cruelly swirls.

Editor's Note

The manuscript for this book arrived in a state far from what one would expect of a finished work. It bore signs of hasty assembly, and some pages, regrettably, were missing. Despite this, the power of the work shone through, and the task of assembling it for publication felt necessary, albeit daunting.

Our efforts to reach out to William for guidance and clarification have been met with troubling silence. We regret to inform you that there are reports suggesting he has gone missing during his travels abroad, adding a sombre note of urgency to our efforts to bring his work to the public.

In light of these circumstances, we have chosen to publish the manuscript as it arrived, incomplete but undeniably potent. To withhold it felt untenable - its vivid exploration of our reality, and of realms unknown, through the lens of our seemingly innocuous childhoods, demanded to be shared.

As you delve into "The Grimoire of Forgotten Fairytales," it is our hope that you will find yourself captivated and inspired by William's discoveries and although we cannot confirm or deny the veracity of William's warning about it's contents, we hope you peruse this book with care.

Sincerely,

Edmund Berringer
Editor

Contents

Foreword

As I write this, my hands tremble slightly, betraying both the anticipation and anxiety that have been my companions since embarking on this remarkable journey. I am but a humble collector, a gatherer of the forgotten and the overlooked, but the task I have undertaken is anything but ordinary. The stories within this tome are the products of my pursuit of a truth concealed in the very fabric of our world, a testament to my travels to the farthest reaches of the earth and the deepest corners of history. They are my gift to you. They are "The Grimoire of Forgotten Fairytales."

My journey began innocently enough: a vague interest in ancient folklore, the desire to decipher the stories that our ancestors whispered around fires, under the open stars. However, as I delved deeper, I was drawn into a world that exists in the shadows of our own, a world steeped in ancient wisdom and inexplicable wonder. In the dense, silent forests of Scandinavia, in the mysterious, haunting depths of Celtic caves, in the sun-scorched earth of the Australian outback, I found verses and riddles sung, spoken, and murmured by voices long silenced.

These tales are not the sugar-coated fantasies that we share with our children before bedtime. They are raw and pure, vibrant with the pulse of the ancient world. Each line in these stories thrums with a power that cannot be tamed by time or place. They are the echoes of a past where magic was as real as the air we breathe, where the universe hummed with a harmony that many of us have forgotten.

The nursery rhymes that we innocently recite carry within them the remnants of spells and enchantments that have been diluted by time. The riddles we solve for amusement bear the weight of wisdom passed down through countless generations. As I unearthed these long-forgotten narratives, spells, and riddles from their ancient resting places, I became painfully aware of the latent power within them. Each word, each verse, serves as a key, opening doors to realms beyond our comprehension.

Each tale and riddle in this grimoire was found etched into the stones of age-old ruins, written on parchment as brittle as autumn leaves, or sometimes whispered to me by a wind that seemed to carry the weight of a thousand years. Many a time, I could almost feel the eyes of unseen guardians watching me from the shadows as I uncovered these fragments of an older, wilder world.

I present this grimoire to you with a sense of awe and a pang of trepidation. The narratives, spells, and riddles within are potent; they vibrate with the energy of the ancients. They are doors to a past when the line between the mortal realm and the magical was but a faint whisper. They are the whispered secrets of the universe, concealed in rhyme and veiled in riddles.

But with these gifts come warnings. These tales, riddles, and spells are not merely words. They are the keys to ancient knowledge, the gateways to realms unseen, and to read them is to dance with forces that we scarcely understand. Treat them with the respect they command; tread carefully on the path they illuminate.

And so, dear reader, I present you with "The Grimoire of Forgotten Fairytales." As you turn these pages, you walk in the footsteps of our ancestors, entering a world of whispers and shadows, of magic and myth. I welcome you to this journey, but I urge caution. After all, these tales are not easily forgotten, and the world they reveal is not for the faint of heart.

Upon the isle of Whispers,
hushed, a ring of stones unveils,

Where stands statues of legend,
beneath the island's gales.

In their grip, the endless threads,
of universe and dread,

Eons hold no dominion, Where time itself has fled.

Eyes vacant, yet filled With stars,
their arms are held aloft,

In the silent sanctuary,
Where the spheres softly cough.

Stones Whispering tales, of the Summoners' might,

Who conjure up the day, and dispel the shivering night.

They, the cosmic sentinels,
stand stoic under starlight's glow,

Guardians of eternity, against the abyss they stow.

In their hands,
rest the Weft of dimensions intertwine,

As the pulsating universe, in their palms align.

From the edge of oblivion, Where spectres thrive,

They hold us aloft, and keep us alive.

Ever Watchful, they endure,
in the heart of the throbbing sea,

Where even light drowns, in its inky spree.

They are the Summoners, of the Dread so immense,

Stewards of reality, our cosmic defence.

A tale etched in stone, under moon's pale glow,

Their names anon are inscribed here below:

Daniel "Dadstar" Thompson

Cheryl R Kennedy

Nikki Youngman

David Irvine

Mike Faulkner

Luke Green

Skye Batchelor

Darman Friestad

Ari the Alchemist

Natalia Webber

Caleb Sapp

HighPriestKadaj

Jeff Miller

Ilsa "Holly Noel" Maguellal

Abby

Amber Bartlett

Amber Harrison

Scott Houge

Brianna Van Zandt

Jordan Gonyea

Conner Meyers-Claybourn

TheDrunkMonk22

Jared Brandon

Zack

See a penny, pick it up,
All day long you'll have good luck.
Catch a star and make a wish,
Greet the dawn with sunlight's kiss.
In the forest, seek a door,
Opens to a forgotten lore.
Catch the glow of a fairy's flight,
In the heart of the darkest night.
Wake a shadow deep and old,
In the gloom it's secrets unfold.
Pick a relic, dark and cursed,
Feel the universe reversed.
Find a mirror, black and cold,
Reflecting all old tales untold.
Watch the stars in patterns shift,
Feel reality start to rift.
See a Penny, make your claim,
But beware the endless game,
Once a charm of simple luck,
Now a door to madness struck.

Hickory, dickory, dock,
The mouse ran up the clock.
The clock struck one,
The mouse ran down,
Hickory, dickory, dock.

Quiver, shiver, shock,
In the shadows, demons flock.
The stars struck two,
Reality skewed,
Quiver, shiver, shock.

Eclipse, abyss, lock,
Through the keyhole, horrors mock.
Time struck three,
In the void, echoes plea,
Eclipse, abyss, lock.

Cosmic, chaotic, stock,
Round the clock, the old ones walk.
The void struck four,
At sanity's shore,
Cosmic, chaotic, stock.

Hickory, dickory, dock,
In the madness, we are caught.
The end has begun,
Under a blackened sun,
Hickory, dickory, dock.

Sticks and stones may break my bones,
But names will never hurt me,
Yet in the murmur of the olden tones,
Lies the truth that sets us free.

Words, mere whispers in the wind,
Hold a power unseen,
In the echo of a name, my friend,
Awakens magic, ancient and keen.

An innocent utterance, soft and light,
Can call forth a spectral host,
Stones may shatter in the night,
Yet, in names lies the true cost.

Sticks and stones may wound the skin,
A pang that will soon desert,
But a name can stir the darkness within,
Unleash a pain covert.

Beware the old power of spoken words,
More potent than any bite,
For sticks and stones may break my bones,
But a name is an ancient rite.

A Riddle

Within my core, the abyss is held,

An echo of a realm dispelled.

A window to the dark unknown,

Reflecting truths to madness sown.

I do not blink, yet always stare,

Into depths that ensnare.

What am I that bridges night and day,

A silent watcher in the cosmic play?

Directions

Bow before the Veiled Lady, her visage shrouded in pall,
Honor her with silence, let no utterance fall.
In the hollow of the twisted tree,
Where shadows dance and play,
You'll find a key of bone, hold it tight, let not your grip sway.

As the Crow of Midnight calls, three times upon the ebon air,
Turn your back to the Moon's cold glare, courage you must wear.
Across the sea of obsidian glass, row with an oar of ash,
Beware the whispering waves that tell tales of worlds long past.

At the shrine of forgotten echoes, lay down the bone key,
With a prayer to the silent Gods,
Who watch from beneath the sea,
As the stars weep silver tears, open the Door of Dreams,
Enter with not fear in heart, for things are not as they seem.

Tread the Path of Eternal Shadows,
With neither torch nor guide,
Trust the darkness that enfolds, it is in you to confide.
At journey's end, a Chalice waits,
filled with the Slumbering Mist,
Drink deeply, fear not the taste, on your brow the Lady's kiss.

One for sorrow,
Two for joy,
Three for a girl,
Four for a boy,

Five for silver,
Six for gold,
Seven for a secret, never to be told.

Eight for a tale the stars have spun,
Nine for a gate that can't be undone,

Ten for a river of forgotten lore,
Eleven for a key to the spectral door.

Twelve for a mirror that reflects the night,
Thirteen for a beast that lives in spite,

Fourteen for a realm beyond our reach,
Fifteen for a speech no tongue can teach.

Sixteen for a dream trapped in stone,
Seventeen for the old god's hollow moan,

Eighteen for the abyss that gazes back,
Nineteen for the cosmic, formless wrack.

Twenty for a magpie's final verse,
In a universe where shadows converse.
The end of the rhyme, the start of the dread,
Where not a single word is said.

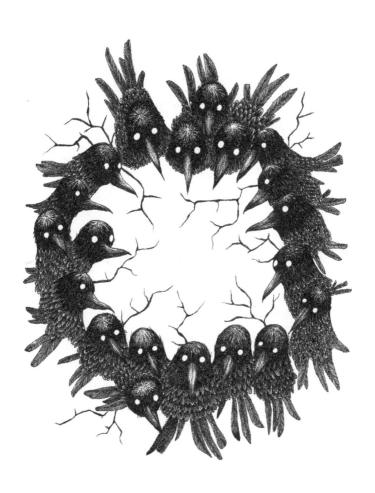

One, two, buckle my shoe;
Three, four, knock at the door;

Five, six, pick up sticks;
Seven, eight, lay them straight;

Nine, ten, light the sage;
Eleven, twelve, unlock the cage.

Thirteen, fourteen, draw the unseen;
Fifteen, sixteen, in the circle pristine;

Seventeen, eighteen, recite the creed;
Nineteen, twenty, offering's aplenty.

The ritual is done, the god has won,
In the echo of stars, our world undone.

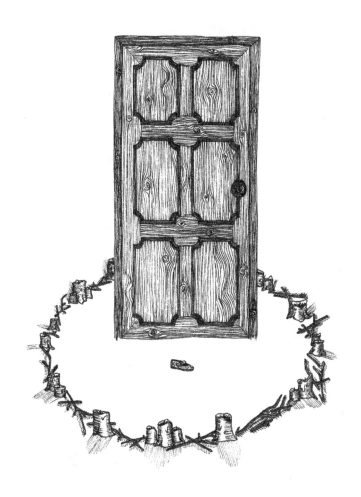

As my feet pressed deeper into the emerald stillness of the Scandinavian forests, a silence so profound swallowed me. An ancient whisper seemed to echo within these primeval trees, the air humming with unseen currents. The sensation of unseen eyes on me was not entirely unpleasant; rather, it was a familiar comfort. I felt observed, studied, perhaps even known.

In this unending hush, I stumbled upon a curious stone formation, almost entirely claimed by the forest's relentless grasp. Worn and weathered, the stones seemed to hum with an energy as old as the universe itself. They were arranged in a peculiar pattern, reminiscent of the celestial bodies above. Underneath the cloak of moss and ivy, I discerned what seemed like crude inscriptions. They spoke of something — or someone — referred to as 'The Watcher in the Woods.'

Transcribing the weathered etchings onto parchment, I began to uncover the tale of this Watcher. A figure of Scandinavian folklore, he was known as a guardian spirit, a protector of the natural world. Said to reside within the heart of the oldest tree, he witnessed the forest's every secret, guarded its sacred lore, and kept a vigilant watch over its timeless rhythm.

The deeper I delved into the Watcher's tale, the stronger grew the sensation of being watched. It

Wasn't fear that took root within me, rather a strange calm, as though I was standing in the centre of a grand, unseen orchestra. The whispering leaves, the rustling undergrowth, the gentle sigh of the wind — it all seemed to form a symphony only the Watcher could conduct.

As nightfall wrapped the forest in her ebon cloak, I found myself reluctant to leave. I lit a small fire and let the warm, dancing flames dispel the creeping shadows. I recited the tale of the Watcher aloud, the words tasting of time and the mystery that dwelt within the trees.

I spoke of his eternal vigil, his pact with the ancient forest spirits, and his solemn duty to maintain the harmony between man and nature. As the last word slipped from my lips, a breathless silence fell, so deep that it seemed as though the very heart of the forest was listening.

In that silence, I felt an unmistakable presence — a profound consciousness that defied human comprehension. I could feel it in the gentle rustle of the leaves, hear it in the distant hoot of an owl, see it in the twinkling dance of the fireflies. It was as though the forest had come alive, stirred into wakefulness by the tale of its guardian.

And then, there it was — a feeling of being observed, yet not with malice or suspicion, but with an ageless wisdom and silent acknowledgement. The Watcher was there, an omnipresent guardian etched into the fabric of the forest, the silent, ceaseless observer in this unending symphony of nature.

As dawn slowly reclaimed the forest, I found myself profoundly altered. I had felt a presence beyond the constraints of our mortal comprehension, experienced a wisdom older than time itself, and had been privy to an ancient tale nestled within the heart of these silent woods.

I packed my belongings, my heart pulsating with the story I had to tell, the tale of the Watcher in the woods. Yet, as I departed, I could still feel his gaze upon me — a reminder of the ancient pact between mankind and nature, a promise of protection, and a silent plea for respect.

The only story I could find passed down about the Watcher, was the one that I present to you on the following page. I share it with you in the context that my experience was altogether less sinister and more fascinating.

If you go down to the woods today,
Beyond the path where the sunlight plays,
Beneath the ancient, gnarled boughs, it lays,
An unseen watcher in the dappled haze.

If you go down to the woods tonight,
When the moon casts an eerie light,
You'll sense a presence, just out of sight,
That fills your heart with a primal fright.

It whispers in the rustling leaves,
In the shivering cold that makes you grieve,
Amongst the shadows that deceive,
In the woods, where nightmares weave.

If you go down to the woods, beware,
Of the silent gaze, the chilling stare,
In the quiet woods, it's always there,
The entity that strips you bare.

So tread softly on the mossy floor,
For the woods are not as they were before,
The watcher waits, forevermore,
In the woods, beyond the door.

A Riddle

In shadows deep it takes its stand,

Neither beast, nor yet a man.

Eyes that gleam like fallen stars,

A voice that hums from worlds afar.

It walks in dreams, yet never sleeps,

To mortal minds, its secret seeps.

What is it that whispers through the night,

Emanating endless fright?

An incantation presented exclusively for SILENT academia

Materials
- A vial of midnight dew collected under a moonless sky
- A strand of hair from the one you wish to bind
- Three drops of your blood, drawn in the silence of the night
- A candle, as dark as the heart of the abyss
- A parchment, inscribed with the ancient script of the Elders
- An obsidian blade, kissed by the northern winds

Step one: In the solitude of night, gather your materials, preparing your mind for the arcane.
Step two: Ignite the abyssal candle, casting a spectral glow upon the parchment.
Step three: Carefully, let your blood fall onto the strand of hair, and the vial's dew.
Step four: Recite the incantation, wielding the obsidian blade with reverence, inscribing the air with unseen runes.

Beneath the stars, in silence, I call,
Elders' script, guide my thrall.
By midnight dew and obsidian's might,
Into the abyss, I cast my plight.

Blood of mine, and strand entwine,
Sewn together, our fates align.
Bound by silence, your will shall bend,
In the quiet dark, from beast to friend.

Upon the twilight's final gleam,
We drift away in the realm of dream,
A pact we keep, as day turns dim,
With the noble Lord of Slumber's hymn.

In cloaks of starlight, soft and warm,
'Gainst waking world's tumult and storm,
His tender grace, a solace sweet,
Where heartbeats slow and breathings meet.

"Give to me," he kindly implores,
"A slice of life, not more than fours,
Twice each night, in restful flight,
And I'll guard thy dreams with all my might."

Eight hours we offer, nothing more,
Leaving our conscious selves at the door,
A generous tithe, our willing yield,
In his celestial, dream-spun field.

He shapes our dreams with artist's hand,
In realms unseen by waking land,
We glide through skies of crystal blue,
And taste the honeyed morning dew.

We dance with moons, and chat with stars,
Free from the world's unending wars,
We sail on clouds, and leap on rain,
In his domain, no fear, no pain.

Oh, sweet surrender, this contract's seal,
In morning's light, refreshed we feel,
He tends to us with gentle care,
Renewing strength for day's affair.

A third of life, in slumber's keep,
Is not lost, but sown deep,
A mystic pact, in twilight's trust,
To the Lord of Dreams, sleep we must.

So to his kingdom, we retire,
Kindled by the moonbeam's fire,
In trust we sleep, in peace we rest,
In the arms of Slumber, we are blessed.

Red sky at night, shepherd's delight.
Red sky in the morning, shepherd's warning.

Black stars on high, owls cease their cry,
Purple haze at dawn, shepherd's truth is drawn.

Green comet streaks, reality shrieks.
Silver mist at noon sings a spectral tune.

Ebon rainbow arcs, the silence harks.
Turquoise clouds swirl as dimensions unfurl.

Crimson sea churns as the universe turns.

Red sky in the morning, shepherd's warning,
Under an obsidian sky, shepherd's sanity lies.

Black sun ascends as space time rends,
And in the shepherd's tale, the universe ends.

Tinker, tailor, soldier, sailor,
Rich man, poor man, beggar man, thief.

Ploughman, painter, preacher, jailer,
Bard, scribe, whisperer of grief.

Alchemist, prophet, enchanter, spy,
Dreamer, jester, falcon's eye.

Veil-ripper, gatekeeper, a serpent's lie,
Watcher, warden, shadowed cry.

Gloom-caster, nightmare weaver,
Dark lantern, silent deceiver,

Eldritch seer of the under-feather,
Twilight bringer of stormy weather.

Moon-mad scholar, star-born hound,
Key-keeper of the shadowed ground,

Void walker, secret keeper,
Eternal vigil, dreamless sleeper.

Crone whisperer, faceless queen,
Puppet master behind the unseen,

Song-singer of the midnight sun,
Keeper of the Forgotten One.

Archivist of the cyclopean tome,
Scribe of the echo in elder's bone,

Silent sentinel of the abyss,
Witness of the final, unholy kiss.

Mirror-gazer, cryptic sparrow,
Guide of the path ever-narrow,

Last whisperer of the ancient chant,
Knower of the seed that can't.

Squid-headed scribe of the eternal deep,
Warden of secrets that shadows keep,

Walker 'twixt the stars' cold blight,
Singer in the endless night.

Prism-bearer of the inky black,
Harbinger of the universe's wrack,

Time-keeper of the celestial tear,
The last echo of cosmic fear.

So, round and round, the roles We play,
In this grand theatre of night and day,

Tinker, tailor, soldier, sailor,
Darker still, the cosmic jailer.

A Riddle

A circle ancient, silent and still,

Guarded by the watchful hill.

Unseen forces, an eldritch will,

A puzzle left for minds to fill.

What mortal hand or mortal eye,

Could frame such mystery 'neath the sky?

Where shadows dance and spirits lie,

Beneath the stars, it stands so high.

Born of earth and starlit song,

It has been here, oh so long.

In this place of right and wrong,

Where does this monolith belong?

In ancient times, 'neath the cosmic veil,
There danced a god, both hearty and hale.
Named Boone, a trickster filled with mirth,
Old as the stars, old as the earth.

He danced and laughed, to all a friend,
Yet, the others sought a different end.
Power they craved, glory, and might,
They cast Boone out into the night.

Rejected, scorned, Boone's heart grew cold,
His laughter stilled, his spirit bold.
A plan he devised, twisted and slick,
A trick for the gods, cruel and quick.

He whispered words in the void so vast,
A spell that echoed, a shadow cast.
From the corners where the old gods dream,
He summoned a force, a spectral gleam.

A mirror it was, but not as we know,
It reflected not faces, but the soul's glow.
Each god beheld their truth laid bare,
Their greed and pride, an empty stare.

The gods, they shrieked, they roared, they cried,
In their own monstrous nature, they could not hide.
Boone laughed again, a sound filled with spite,
And disappeared into the everlasting night.

As the peculiar scent of ancient tomes filled my lungs, I found myself lost in the labyrinth of a forgotten library, buried beneath the cobwebbed streets of a silent city. Its shadowy halls held an eerie silence, occasionally broken by the rustle of parchment or the quiet scrape of time upon stone. There, amidst the dust-laden air, I discovered a weathered page - an intricately detailed illustration of forms so surreal they defied comprehension.

Creatures, otherworldly and grotesque, twined and twisted together in a disarray of haunting beauty. An image so chaotic, yet eerily mesmerising. The beings seemed to undulate from the parchment, their ethereal bodies tangled in a dance that transcended mortal understanding. A chill coursed down my spine, the enormity of their alien existence echoing in the stillness.

Accompanying the image, there were words inked with a hand long stilled, yet they seemed alive with an electric current. An eight-line verse that resonated with a chilling eeriness. It claimed to hold the essence of what the image unveiled:

In depths unknown, Where shadows dance,
Born of chaos, not of chance.
Entities tWine in cosmic plight,
Underneath the starless night.

Unseen eyes in silence stare,
In our World, yet not quite there.
In this image, truth's disguise,
Behold the Dance of Unseen Eyes.

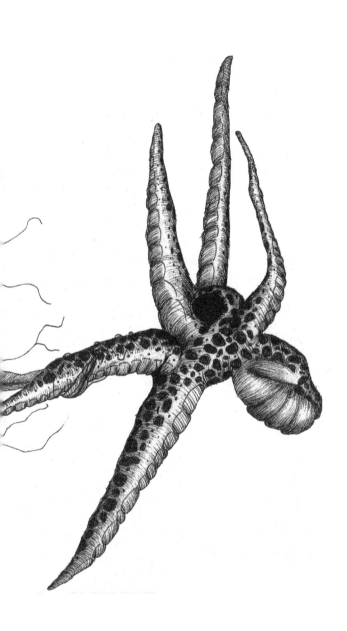

Old Mother Hubbard
Went to the cupboard,
To give the poor dog a bone:
When she got there,
The cupboard was bare,
And so the poor dog had none.

She went back to her chair,
With a lingering stare,
At the shadows the candlelight cast.
In the deafening quiet,
An unholy riot,
Echoes of a time long past.

Once, her cupboard abundant,
Now rendered redundant,
Bore testament to time's cruel jest.
Her loyal companion,
In earthly dominion,
Grew restless in his endless quest.

In the dead of the night,
Under faint moonlight,
The dog began to morph and distort.
No longer a hound,
But a beast unbound,
In this harrowing, spectral sport.

His eyes glowed amber,
His form, it encumbered,
The room that once was their home.
Old Mother Hubbard,
With fear she shuddered,
At the creature from the monochrome.

A tale once benign,
Over the line,
In the realm of dread and dismay.
Take heed, dear friend,
For stories can bend,
In the most disquieting way.

On St. Catherine's crest of green,
A curious mark upon the scene.
A labyrinth cut into the chalk,
Whispers of a tale they talk.

A wayward boy, his path astray,
Banished to the hill one day.
Alone, he tread the summer's heat,
To the tune of his heart's lonesome beat.

In the breadth of solitude's embrace,
A wild design he began to trace.
Miz-Maze, a puzzle in the green,
A sight in the chalk, seldom seen.

Each turn and twist, a careful plight,
A manifestation of his inner fight.
The boy was but a simple pawn,
In the hands of The Enigma, drawn.

The pattern etched in turf and stone,
Mirrored a truth, in cosmic tone.
His mortal plight, a tragic play,
On the stage of the Enigma's array.

The final day of freedom's reign,
Brought an end to the boy's pain.
Some say, in the river's deep,
He sought his eternal sleep.

Yet in the Miz-Maze's winding design,
Lies a tale of the divine.
The boy, once lost, found his place,
In the Enigma's cosmic embrace.

His tragedy, as the river did weep,
In the hill's heart, secrets seep.
The Miz-Maze remains, a cryptic scar,
A boy's tale, whispered from afar.

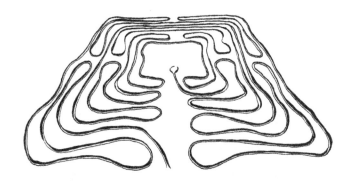

"You've made your bed, now lie in it,"
So goes the old, judgmental bit.
Yet in your slumber, shadows flit,
Reality begins to split.

The fabric of existence tears,
Into the abyss, your soul it ensnares.
A pact you've made has reawakened,
A debt you owe must now be taken.

Lying down, you're made aware,
Of the chains, ethereal and bare.
In this prison, stripped you stare,
Into the eyes of your nightmare.

Gaze upon Bond, the Eternal Chain,
His realm your bed, your realm his bane.
In dreams, his realm begins to drain,
The essence of your mortal plane.

Your slumber, now an endless plight,
Beneath the cloak of starless night.
In the bed you've made, devoid of light,
Sleeps the truth of cosmic fright.

The end of dreams, becomes his might,
In Bond's realm, there is no right.
You've made your bed, now every night,
You lie in it, beneath his sight.

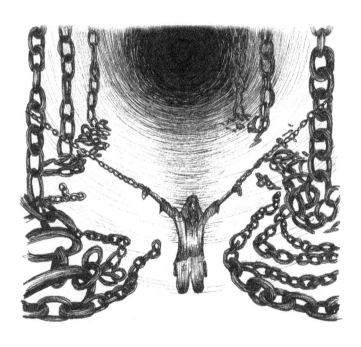

It's raining, it's pouring,
The old man is snoring,
He went to bed and bumped his head,
And couldn't get up in the morning.

The old man's slumber, not in vain,
He is a link in the cosmic chain.
A sigil scribed in the pouring rain,
A covenant with the eldritch plane.

The rain kept on pouring,
In dreams, Old Gods were roaring,
He fell in slumber and joined their number,
As is counted by the scoring.

It's singing, it's purring,
In the depths, something is stirring,
The old man listens, his mind a-glisten,
To the calls of cosmic burdens.

His snoring in sync with the planet's humming,
A melody of the awakened coming.
He went to bed, a simple thing,
And rose as a pawn to the ancient king.

Mary, Mary, quite contrary,
How does your garden grow?
With seeds of whispers, nurtured in dread,
Where the eldritch shadows flow.
Tendrils creep and stalks ascend,
To a sky that shrieks in hues,
Of colours unseen in the light of day,
Baring secrets un-pursued.

Silver bells echo a mournful toll,
That seep into the bones,
Cockleshells cast of iridescent despair,
A monument to cosmic unknowns.
From each dark corner,
The eyeless blooms leer,
Sucking the light and joy,
Feeding on every fear.

In the heart of the garden,
Where none dare tread,
Lies a well of darkness,
A font of dread.
Its water mirrors
An abomination unkind,
A visage of your deepest horror,
Enough to shatter any mind.

Mary, Mary, quite contrary,
You ask how my garden grows?
Beneath the moon's pale scorn,
Where the river of madness flows.
So come with me, my sweet,
Let's sow another seed,
In the garden of the cosmos,
Where sanity recedes.

"Rain, rain, go away, come again another day,"
The chant of children in their play.
Unbeknownst to them, a darker way,
Their words awake a shadow grey.

"Rain, rain, do heed their plea,
But bring instead a darker sea."
From the abyss, the words echo free,
A prayer to gods man shouldn't see.

"Rain, rain," the chant takes hold,
Innocence, the key to the old.
Reality twists, the skies unfold,
A child's rhyme, a prophecy foretold.

Rain, rain, now here to stay,
The daylight drowned, the night can play.
Awakened horrors start their fray,
In a world where children's words hold sway.

Incy Wincy Spider climbed up the water spout,
Down came the rain and washed the spider out,
Out came the sun and dried up all the rain,
So Incy Wincy Spider climbed up the spout again.

His heart was seething, now, full of vengeful dread,
This time he would conquer, weaving thick his thread.
The spout would be his castle, his citadel of fright,
By sun or by the storm, he would rule the day and night.

A king, here, in his web, his reign a gruesome thrill,
He grew, grotesque and massive, feasting on each kill.
His eyes, a dozen nightmares, his fangs dripping with spite,
No more a tiny spider, but a monstrous beast of night.

Incy Wincy no more, he is the Spider King,
In his dreadful realm, and terror, all he brings.
So hark! Beware the water spout, once so clean and plain,
Lest you stir the wrath of the King's wicked reign.

The suggestion from my friend, more of an offhand joke than a serious proposal, was to explore the labyrinthine catacombs beneath the renowned Highgate Cemetery. At first, the idea seemed somewhat contrived, a plot in a dime-a-dozen horror novel, but my curiosity was not so easily quelled. Given my interest in old rhymes and the enigmatic whispers of ancient magic, I found myself drawn, like a moth to flame, to the cold, sepulchral embrace of the crypts.

Wandering through the subterranean network of narrow passages, my footsteps echoed loudly, reverberating off the damp stone walls. I walked in a world caught in an eternal twilight, my only source of light the dim, flickering torch I held. The corridors snaked away in all directions, their paths twisting and turning in a disorienting maze.

Despite carrying the most up to date map I could find of the place, I stumbled across a tunnel that didn't seem to be marked. Perhaps I was just reading the map incorrectly, or perhaps I was lost. Whether by choice or driven on by an invisible force, I found myself venturing into the darkness. I wandered down that tunnel for some time, although time itself seemed to become elusive, as though the minutes were hours and the hours mere moments. Was it twenty minutes? Or had several hours passed? The shadows did not yield an answer.

Without Warning, the close confines of the tunnel opened up into a vast, cavernous darkness so complete it seemed to drink up the weak light from my torch. Stepping warily forward, I beheld an immense, hollowed-out chamber, its soaring ceiling lost in the darkness above, its walls carved intricately with symbols and signs that I could not identify. It was a spectacle unlike anything I had ever seen. It had the feeling of a lost chapel of some kind or perhaps a temple of some long-lost civilisation or forgotten cult.

Strangely-shaped artefacts, eerie in their silent, stone vigil, stood on pedestals scattered around the room. Each one seemed to radiate an odd sense of disquiet, a faint trace of an energy long past. Ascending a grand flight of stone steps, I came across an altar. The sight sent a shiver down my spine. There was something decidedly unsettling about this place.

Yet, it was not these artefacts or the altar that drew my attention. Instead, it was the massive mural behind the altar, an overwhelming work of art painted on the stone. It depicted five... beings? Creatures of some kind, they were of such strangeness and awe that they were at once beautiful and deeply disturbing. To look at them was to feel the ground shift beneath one's feet, the mind's eye struggle to comprehend their forms.

The longer I looked, the more disorienting it became. The five distinct beings seemed both different and somehow the same, resonating with a deep, unsettling sense of familiarity. I stood there, frozen by awe and terror, captivated by the mural's inexplicable allure. There was a sense of madness to the whole scene, a wild, reckless abandon that chills me even now as I recall it.

Eventually, the dread overpowered me. I turned and fled from the underground temple, back through the winding tunnels and into the relative safety of the cemetery grounds. As I emerged, gasping for fresh air, I found that the images and the chilling fear had etched themselves indelibly into my memory.

Most haunting were the words on a plaque below the mural. The echoes of a verse, each line filled with cryptic meaning, each word humming with a power that resonated with the deepest parts of my being. No matter how much I tried to shake them, they clung to the corners of my consciousness, refusing to be forgotten.

Dear reader, I am bound by my purpose to share all I have discovered, yet I implore you, for your own peace of mind, refrain from reading the verse that follows this account. I have included it in this book, not out of reckless curiosity, but because it is my duty to complete this collection. It is a song of power, of dread, and of the inexplicable, a tune I wish I could unhear. If your strength of will allows it, please, do not indulge your curiosity. Let the next page remain unturned.

In the realm of void and silence,
Dwells Kcaraleth the Prime,
Master of forgotten echoes,
Inverting the flow of time.
His form unseen by mortal gaze,
A paradox in itself,
A creature caught between the ticks,
In reality's warped shelf.

T'sini, the Enigma,
Weaves her spectral loom,
In the endless halls of dreaming,
Where shadows thrive and bloom.
Her whispers dance within your thoughts,
A melody most odd,
A symphony of discordance,
Beneath her enigmatic shroud.

Bond, the Eternal Chain,
Lies coiled and waiting deep,
In places where the earth does groan,
And ageless leviathans sleep.
His links bind all creation,
In a serpentine embrace,
A prison of existence,
An unending, cosmic chase.

Riskarr, the VoidWalker,
Strides between the stars,
In spaces black and boundless,
Beyond the world's scars.
His path, a dance of chaos,
His laughter, a shattering roar,
Traversing the abyssal seas,
On reality's trembling floor.

Suthe'rans, the End Scribe,
Writes the universe's demise,
In letters burning with sunset's death,
Under storm-wrought skies.
Each stroke, a civilization's end,
Each word, a planet's fall,
In his tome of finality,
He chronicles the death of all.

Rock-a-bye baby, in the treetop,
When the wind blows, the cradle will rock,
When the bough breaks, the cradle will fall,
And down will come baby, cradle and all.

Oh, hush now dear child, for the wind does speak,
Of ancient horrors, both vile and bleak,
They whisper of entities, in the void's deep,
Awakening as their victims weep.

Cradle of bone, and a lullaby of dread,
Echoes around the treetop bed,
A spectral hand, unseen and cold,
Clasps the baby, in its horrid hold.

The bough doesn't break, it merely bends,
In service to an ancient end,
A nursery rhyme turned requiem,
Under the moon's phantasmic hem.

The cradle falls, into the abyss,
Rocked gently by a cosmic hiss,
Rock-a-bye baby, the stars align,
In the darkness, the old gods dine.

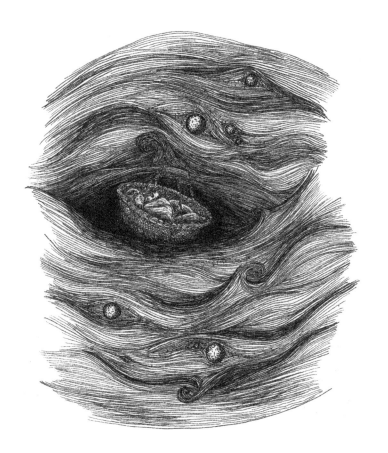

London Bridge is falling down,
Falling down, falling down,
London Bridge is falling down,
My fair lady.

Stone and mortar cannot hold,
Against the tales that ancients told,
Of shadows from the river's fold,
Unseen, yet ever deadly.

Build it up with iron and steel,
Iron and steel, iron and steel,
Stronger, now, with each ordeal,
My fair lady.

But steel will warp, and iron will bend,
To the will of what the deep rivers send,
A darkness that all efforts offend,
With a hunger insatiable.

Build it up with silver and gold,
Silver and gold, silver and gold,
With treasures, many and manifold,
My fair lady.

Yet gold and silver, precious and bright,
Cannot halt the unending night,
That seeks to smother the city's light,
In its eldritch embrace.

Build it up with bones and blood,
Bones and blood, bones and blood,
Drawn from the river's ancient flood,
My fair lady.

A bridge of sacrifice, dark and dread,
A monument to the countless dead,
Who dared to tread where nightmares tread,
In the heart of the shadowed Thames.

London Bridge is falling down,
Falling down, falling down,
But what rises in its stead, will astound,
My fair lady.

A monolith of bone and lead,
A sentinel for the ancient dead,
London Bridge, the city's dread,
An altar to what slumbers below.

Little Boy Blue, come blow your horn,
The sheep's in the meadow, the cow's in the corn.
Where is the boy who looks after the sheep?
He's under the haystack, fast asleep.

But Little Boy Blue, he sleeps not in jest,
For in dreams, he's taken a dark, ghastly quest.
Beyond the meadow, past the corn's golden hue,
Lies a realm of shadows where nightmares accrue.

The horn he once blew, now silent and cold,
Heralds no flock, but secrets untold.
In the distance, an echoing, haunting refrain,
Whispers of beings that exist beyond the mundane.

The sheep and the cows, mere illusions they seem,
As Boy Blue delves deeper into the dream.
The haystack conceals an entrance so vile,
To caverns below, that stretch mile after mile.

There, ancient glyphs on cavernous walls,
Speak of a power that rises and falls.
A cosmic entity, vast and profound,
Whose slumbering presence shakes the ground.

Little Boy Blue, with terror in his eyes,
Realises too late, the awful surprise.
For the horn he once played, was a key, a device,
To awaken the old ones, a perilous price.

So when you hear a horn, soft and low,
Beware the meadow where dark secrets grow.
For Little Boy Blue, now bound to that place,
Guarding a secret, lost in time and space.

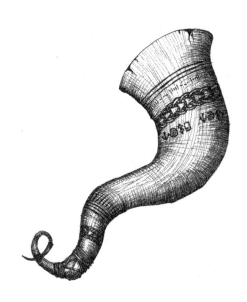

final spell

every wera, a blurt's Jull

each line, a star's last dance

but return
the cosmic

dirge in
the grandeur of
(return) last glance

or of gazing the c

osmic

orbit r it

in the silence of the universe

he writes the final spell

Jutherians the
cloaked in shadows, shroud
her poised above the aging light
his whispers echo loud

in Sunsets death
each burning stroke
Strips a worlds last sigh

It is time to say goodbye
beneath the storm-torn sky

A Riddle

In the deep where shadows dance
and starlight fears to spread,
A creature walks on common ground,
where angels dare not tread.
He swims amidst the everyday,
a herring cloaked in grey,
Shrouded in mundanity,
in twilight's dim array.

He whispers not in ancient tongues,
nor does he call the storm,
Yet in his hands, the world does turn,
in form so simple, so norm.
A riddle wrapped in common cloth,
a mystery mundane,
What is he, this silent one,
who wears the mask of plain?

A Riddle

I began as a mere tremor, a whisper in the void,
A delicate secret, reality's ploy.
Born of a thought, just a murmur in the air,
In the mind's deepest corners, I take my lair.

Unseen I travel, on wings of the word,
The echoes of silence, unheard yet heard.
I rise and grow, a tempest of despair,
In each hushed whisper, I am there.

No walls can contain me, no hands can grasp,
For I am the echo of a cosmic gasp.
I lurk in the shadows, the spaces in between,
A creature of silence, unheard, unseen.

A bearer of truths, a carrier of lies,
In each shared glance, my form can fly.
A Pandora's box, a cosmic jest,
Within the hearts of men, I rest.

DO NOT USE THIS SPELL

Underneath the obsidian night,
Where moonlight fears to fall,
Upon this hour of spectral gloom,
heed this unholy call.
Speak the words of shadowed dread,
in tongues that time forgot,
And weave the threads of cosmic dread,
in this accursed plot.

"Zalthor mandrex oti y'soth,
nekros zanti galathot,
In realms unseen, in chaos born,
Where mortal fears have rot.
Harvest stars of fallen dreams,
and shadows of the night,
Sear the veil of reality,
with this eldritch rite.

K'thun vi lothren emni rast,
bind the essence of the void,
In the silence of the abyss,
Where sanity's destroyed.
Let the heavens tremble,
let the earth beneath us weep,
Call upon the ancient powers,
from their eternal sleep.

Grasp the echo of the scream,
that birthed the universe,
Wield the sorrow of the ages,
in this unhallowed verse.
Dark and terrible the cost,
as day turns into night,
Ensnared within this dire spell,
behold thy dreadful might."

Remember, reader, the chilling cost,
the echo of your sin,
The spell you cast, this fearsome hex,
it festers deep within.
Beware, for power's seductive call,
is a haunting, treacherous song,
And in the dance of shadows dark,
many have been led wrong.

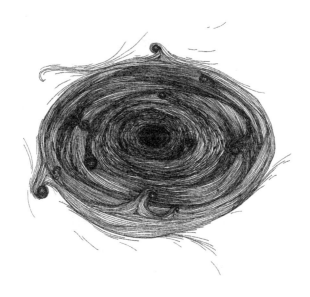

Tom, Tom, the piper's son,
Stole a pig, and away did run;
The pig was eat
And Tom was beat,
And Tom ran crying down the street.

The piper's melody twists and turns,
Across the abyss where the old god burns;
Its eye awakes,
Reality shakes,
And towards the cosmic void, Tom yearns.

Tom, Tom, lost under the sun,
Chased by shadows, his sanity undone;
The pig was feast,
And Tom, the least,
Now Tom's crying has just begun.

In realms unknown, he takes his stride,
Where cosmic horrors in silence reside;
The shadows creep,
And whisperings seep,
And Tom finds there's nowhere left to hide.

In its gaze, Tom sees the night,
A Wash With stars, yet devoid of light;
The silence roars,
Eternity soars,
And Tom becomes a spectral sight.

"Tom, Tom," the old god hums,
Echoing in the celestial drums;
The pig, a rite,
Beneath endless night,
As the cycle of chaos, once more, comes.

Cliff of the old ones

Tunnel entrance

Right leg

The Empty Expanse

Snake pits

Oasis
(Tallest palm points the way)

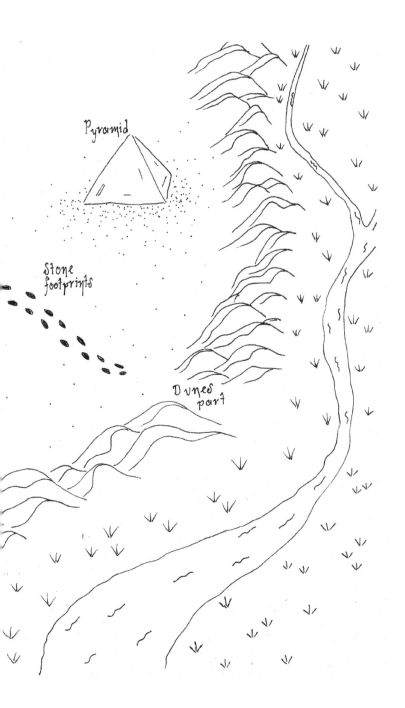

Pyramid

Stone footprints

Dunes part

Diddle, diddle, dumpling, my son John,
Went to bed with his trousers on;
One shoe off, and the other shoe on,
Diddle, diddle, dumpling, my son John.

Twiddle, twiddle, turning, my son John,
In his dreams, our reality is drawn;
One eye open, and the other eye gone,
Twiddle, twiddle, turning, my son John.

Scribble, scribble, symbols, my son John,
In ancient tongues, eldritch whispers spawn;
One moon waning, and the other moon's dawn,
Scribble, scribble, symbols, my son John.

Riddle, riddle, ruminate, my son John,
Unravels cosmos where mortal thoughts are pawns;
One world fading, and the other world yawns,
Riddle, riddle, ruminate, my son John.

Fiddle, fiddle, fragment, my son John,
Through the mirror, his reflection is drawn;
One self here, and the other self beyond,
Fiddle, fiddle, fragment, my son John.

Quibble, quibble, quaking, my son John,
In his hands, the spectral key is worn;
One door closing, and the other door forlorn,
Quibble, quibble, quaking, my son John.

Diddle, diddle, dumpling, my son John,
Wakes in realms where time is scorned;
One shoe off, and the other shoe transformed,
All the worlds shadows have been reborn.
Diddle, diddle, dumpling, my son John.

Wee Willie Winkie runs through the town,
Upstairs and downstairs in his nightgown,
Rapping at the window, crying through the lock,
'Are the children all in bed, for now it's eight o'clock?'

Wee Willie Winkie wanders through the night,
Cloaked in dreams and bathed in starlight.
Knocking on reality, whispering in dread,
"Do you not see the shadows spread?"

Beyond the town, where time stands still,
In cosmic folds of space, the stars spill.
Beneath his nightgown, an ancient seal,
The key to secrets, time will reveal.

His voice echoes in the silent void,
In realms where mortal laws are voided.
"Are the children all asleep, do they not see the clock?
It ticks not for hours, but for epochs that mock."

He runs not through a town,
but through the cosmic web,
Where galaxies spin and celestial ebb.
Through his veil, an awful secret peers,
Reality is not what it appears.

Wee Willie Winkie, an eldritch sprite,
Bound to keep the secret of the eternal night.
"Are the children all in bed?" he weeps,
for he knows the truth,
In the grand cosmic play,
We're but the unseeing youth.

Peter, Peter, pumpkin eater,
Had a wife and couldn't keep her;
He put her in a pumpkin shell,
And there he kept her very well.

Peter, Peter, warden seether,
Had a secret far beneath her.
Inside the pumpkin, dark and swell,
A cosmic terror began to dwell.

That shell, a cage, for what's obscene,
Pulses with life, unseen.
Peter whispers incantations fell,
To the dread that in the pumpkin dwells.

The stars align, the moon turns red,
Reality is hanging by a thread.
Peter, Peter, in nightmare's spell,
Feeds the horror in the pumpkin shell.

Beware the patch when night has fallen,
For from the gourd, dark gods are calling.
Peter, Peter, the silent yeller,
Is but a puppet, to the terror dweller.

The grand old Duke of York,
He had ten thousand men,
He marched them up to the top of the hill,
And he marched them down again.

And when they were up, they were up,
And when they were down, they were down,
And when they were only halfway up,
They were neither up nor down.

And when they were down, they were gone,
Swallowed by the void, their souls withdrawn.
When they were only halfway up,
They were caught in between, a hapless troupe.

Through the gate of the cosmos, where stars align,
A tentacled horror, in darkness it shines.
From the pit beneath the hill, it began to creep,
Awakening nightmares in their silent sleep.

Their march, a ritual, ancient and grim,
To quell the chaos, to silence the din.
The Duke, a coward, had signed a deal,
His men, a sacrifice, to horrors unreal.

For when they are gone, they are lost,
Their doom, the Duke's unending cost.
And when they are only halfway gone,
They are neither here, nor are they yon.

In the realm of madness, where York's men tread,
Lies the boundary 'twixt the living and the dead.
For as they cross, the truth unwinds,
Of the Duke of York, and his march through time.

In the twilight of a midsummer's eve, my journey took me to a forsaken monolith of a bygone era. Beyond the outskirts of an unnamed hamlet in the desolate expanses of North America, it stood — an abandoned airbase, now a spectral monument to an age of iron birds and thunderous engines. The allure of this crumbling citadel was irresistible, a haunting echo that beckoned me towards its bleak silhouette against the crimson sky. How little I knew then of the terror and loss that this decision would bring.

The structures lay abandoned and desolate, but I could still feel the lingering pulse of humanity. Painted by time and weathered by elements, they held silent stories of victory and defeat, of brave hearts and lost souls. Corridors stretched out like yawning chasms, hangars lay silent, no longer reverberating with the roar of monstrous metal beasts, and control towers stared vacantly into the star-studded expanse of the night.

As I ventured deeper into this eerie labyrinth, a sense of dread began to weave it's tendrils around my heart. The air grew denser, and the silence of the place bore down on me, every echo of my footfall screaming in the void of quietude. As I navigated through the disused control tower, a sudden, unbidden gust of wind swept through the empty halls, carrying with it an inhuman whisper that caused the hair on the back of my neck to stand on end.

Suddenly, I felt a heavy presence, as if unseen eyes were watching me from the gloom. A sense of terror gripped me, and my heart hammered within my chest. I could hear the unmistakable sound of faint footfalls echoing my own, an eerie cadence that chilled my blood. The dread grew palpable, choking, stifling, and an icy coldness seeped into my bones. This airbase was no longer just an abandoned relic; it had transformed into a theatre of shadows and unseen terrors. I knew with every fibre of my being, I had to leave. It wanted me to leave.

In my desperate attempts to flee the looming presence, I stumbled, spilling the satchel that had been my constant companion on this journey. My precious collection of loose notes, the fragments of lost verses, ancient riddles, unearthed spells, academic musings and other discoveries immediately scattered in the winds. I scrambled to collect them, but a sudden, mighty gust of wind seemed to swoop in and sweep them away into the hungry jaws of the night. I reached out, but it was too late.

In the spectral twilight realm
Where dreams and nightmares breed,
There danced two faeries, bathed
In love's enchanting mead.
Their hearts entwined in secret knots,
So lush and full of yearning,
Twixt moonbeam castles, singing brooks,
Where starlight keeps on burning.

Harmony was theirs,
A dance to sweetest twilight's hymn,
In that realm of gentle dreams,
On every petal's brim.
But even love's pure resonance,
In lands by no time tainted,
Can fall prey to shadows' lure,
By dread and malice painted.

From deepest abyss they came,
Monstrosities, fear-fraught,
Sowing whispers of deceit
Within their minds, they sought.
A veil of paranoia,
Dark as raven's cursed wing,
Cast upon the faeries' hearts,
Broke their love-forged ring.

In this dark vein, the madness sprung,
A turmoil tempest-borne,
As each believed the other
Had their sacred vows foresworn.
Bitter wrath and sorrow's tears
Replaced their love's sweet song,
In the twilight realm once tranquil,
Everything seemed wrong.

Once lovers pure, now enemies,
In eternal feud engaged,
Battle lines along the dreamscapes,
Hatefully they staged.
Their once shared laughter, echoes now
As chilling, mournful sighs,
In the haunted air of their twilight realm,
Where no sunlight lies.

Their faerie forces clash beneath
An ever-twisted moon,
In a war that cycles endlessly,
Neither late nor soon.
The shimmering tears of shattered love
Do feed the spectral river,
Where their echoed cries do resonate
With an eternal shiver.

Theirs is a tale of love and loss,
A never-ending sorrow,
Bound by cosmic powers
To clash until the morrow.
Forever in this dance of doom,
Their heartstrings harshly severed,
Two faeries eternally at war,
Whose love was once forever.

In the cosmos, their tale whispers,
A solemn, dire creed,
Of love consumed by madness,
By Riskarr's darkened seed.
In dawn's mournful melody,
A lamentation woven,
Of two faeries, once in love,
By eternal feud, now broken.

A Riddle

In the vast expanse I float and spin,

A blue-green orb where life begins.

Yet beneath my tranquil, sunlit face,

Lie secrets old, and a darker space.

Mountains high and oceans deep,

Upon my skin, they rise and steep.

Yet within my core, there stirs a dread,

Of ancient beings, long thought dead.

By day, a beacon, by night, a curse,

For in my shadows, cosmos' converse.

To fathom my depths is to know despair,

For I am the cradle, the void, the snare.

What am I, with secrets worth,

Both the cradle and tomb of life's birth?

A Riddle

In the shroud of night, it clings so tight,
A canvas vast, pale and sheer.
Upon it dance, both chance and fate,
Drawing joy, love, hope, and fear.

It masks the void, where souls deployed,
Find secrets, raw and deep.
Yet it can tear, with just a flare,
And secrets it can't keep.

In every crease, stories cease,
Yet begin anew each day.
It binds the bone, calls body home,
Yet time will wear away.

Elders whisper of its tether,
A barrier to realms unknown.
Yet in their chants, a dark advance,
Its truth, in horror, shown.

What binds the soul, makes mortals whole,
Yet tears and fades with each breath?

Jack and Gill went up the hill
To fetch a pail of water;
Jack fell down and broke his crown
And Gill came tumbling after.

Not sun nor rain, now stars took reign,
Poor Gill, she felt a wretched ache.
Chasing Jack, she cried "Alack!"
As he slipped into a twisted lake.

The pail, to the brink with cosmic ink,
Began to hum and shift.
Melding the ground, all around,
Into a hushed nightmare's rift.

Gill followed then, in the darkest den,
Where ancient, dreaming horrors sleep.
And the echoes lied as her weeping died,
To taunt the hill, where shadows seep.

Some say up the hill, they venture still,
With spectral innocence forever.
Take heed dear friend, beware the water's end,
And if you go, then go together.

In every shadow, lurking still,
Constant it's gaze, against your will,
All around, in silent wait,
Never blinking, 'til it seals your fate.
Silent whispers, in the night,
Echoes of an ancient rite,
Eyes unseen, yet always near,
Yearning, pulling, drawing near.
Observing you, both day and night,
Underneath burning sun and cold moonlight.

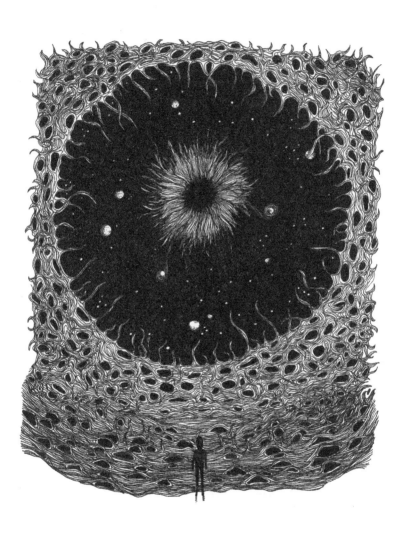

"The early bird catches the worm," we're taught,
Yet in this wisdom, a sinister thought.

In the birds' song, there echoes a call,
To unseen forces that rise and fall.
The worm it seeks, not of this earth,
A creature of incomprehensible worth.

Caught from the soil of a spectral plane,
Reality twists, begins to wane.
Beneath the sun, the bird takes flight,
Unaware it has invoked an ancient blight.

The worm it holds is a cosmic key,
Unlocks the door to an eldritch sea.
The early bird, under the morning's gleam,
Awakens the dwellers of a nightmare's dream.

The bird's innocent chirp belies the truth,
Invoking forces beyond our youth.
In the dance of cosmos, in dawn's soft light,
The early bird awakens the night.

Magpie, magpie,
What shall it be today?
Sun of yellow, silvery moon,
Or dreary clouds of grey?

Magpie, magpie,
What secrets do you hold?
Of tales forgotten, of futures bleak,
Of cryptic myths of old?

Magpie, magpie,
Why do you caw so low?
Whispers of doom, a haunting tune,
From a time so long ago.

Magpie, magpie,
What have you seen tonight?
A starry void, a world destroyed,
Or elder beings of fright?

Deep in your eyes, the universe lies,
A gateway to the vast unknown.
To realms of dread, where souls are led,
And nevermore are shown.

Magpie, magpie,
Why do you perch so near?
With a chilling stare, you declare,
You are the harbinger of fear.

The sun grows dim, as you sing your hymn,
A dirge for all to hear.
For in your song, the World's gone Wrong,
And the end is truly here.

Beware the seeker of olden verse,
For in their pursuit lies an ancient curse.
Pages bound in forgotten lore,
Unleash a shadow evermore.

The spoken word, a dangerous act,
Reality bends, in fact, it cracks.
Invoking echoes of a timeless sea,
You become a part of the cosmic decree.

To buy or barter such a tome,
Is to invite the dark unknown.
Innocent at first, it seems,
Soon you're entwined in nightmare's dreams.

Gathering words of the eldritch past,
Ensures your breath might be your last.
For in the abyss where verses sleep,
The old ones stir, they begin to creep.

To share these tales, a grave mistake,
For every word is a seal you break.
Each rhyme, a step into the deep,
Where ancient horrors awake from sleep.

So heed this Warning, let it ring clear,
In ancient Words, there's much to fear.
Whether found, bought, or given as a boon,
Such verses herald nothing but doom.

Printed in the USA
CPSIA information can be obtained
at www.ICGtesting.com
LVHW042108080224
771342LV00002B/126

9 781739 516406